VISUAL VEXATIONS

VISUAL
VEXATIONS

Devised by
David J. Bodycombe

BARNES
&NOBLE
BOOKS
NEW YORK

2004 Barnes & Noble Books

ISBN 0 7607 5470 5

Printed and bound in Singapore

04 05 06 07 08 09 M 9 8 7 6 5 4 3 2 1

INTRODUCTION

The question I'm asked most often is 'Where do you get all your ideas from?' A quick back-of-the-envelope calculation confirms that in my writing career to date I've penned somewhere in the region of 10,000 different puzzles and it's growing all the time. There will be quite a few puzzle authors – particularly crossword compilers – that can beat this, but it's still a large enough figure for most people to be taken aback.

The answer is to look. Look at everything around you. Telephone keypads, mirrors, bar codes, coins, road signs, calculators, sports results, planets and even paper bags... These are all perfectly ordinary, everyday objects, yet if I look at them with an open mind, something will come to me.

For example, if we considered the tiles on a bathroom or the bricks in a wall, we could do something with that pattern. Maybe the tiles could contain numbers on their perimeters, or maybe a letter could appear on each brick. Maybe it's a matter of tracing a route around the outlines. These are some of the basic inroads to creating some original puzzles.

But I note that you're not here to write puzzles today, you're here to solve them. Nevertheless, you should look at these 100 puzzles carefully for they are visual in nature. You will be mainly tested on your powers of observation and imagination, although there are the occasional number and word-based challenges too, to keep things interesting. And be warned that there is a good sprinkling of puzzles that could benefit from some lateral thinking too.

So keep your eyes open and enjoy the view.

David J. Bodycombe

This is a standard projection map of the Atlantic Ocean. Of the possibilities offered, which flight covers the shortest distance?

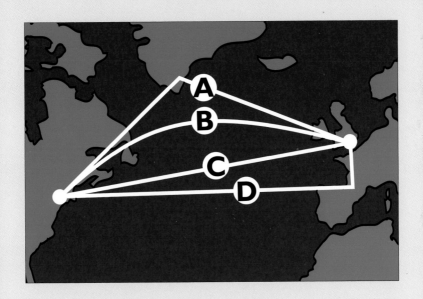

Jonathan likes taking part in scavenger hunts, the activity where you have to retrieve a number of disparate objects in the hope of getting the most points.

On one hunt, he brought back the following items and noticed they all had something in common. What is the common link?

How many arrows can be seen here?

These are the letters of which ten-letter word?

We'll help you by saying that no letters overlap.

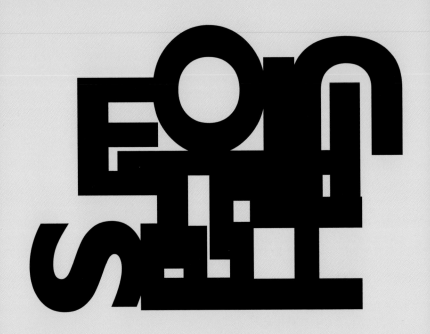

How many spots on a standard gaming die also have a spot in the same position on the opposite face?

In other words, if you were to drill through one spot on the front face, the drill would emerge through a spot on the back face.

Use these two triangles in some combination to discover a well-known phrase:

Rigger Toni delivers pizza for a takeaway. He needs to cut up this Cardiac Supreme for eight customers. Each customer needs exactly the same area of pizza and isn't fussy about how much crust they receive.

How can Toni divide up the pizza into eight equal pieces using three cuts of a knife without rearranging the pizza at any stage?

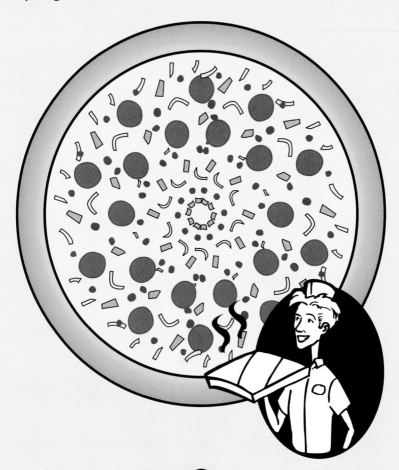

Hannah was getting a little fed up of her darling kid brother pinching all her toys and books. So, one day she had a rubber stamp made with her name on it. She could now merrily stake her claim to all her property.

What was the slight problem with this plan?

This eye-catching design has a clever mathematical property. What proportion of the design is blue?

Which two letters of the alphabet have been cut out of this square?

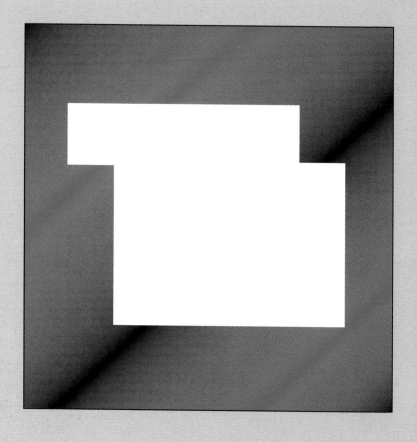

What unique property is shared by triangles, squares and hexagons that does not apply to any other regular polygon?

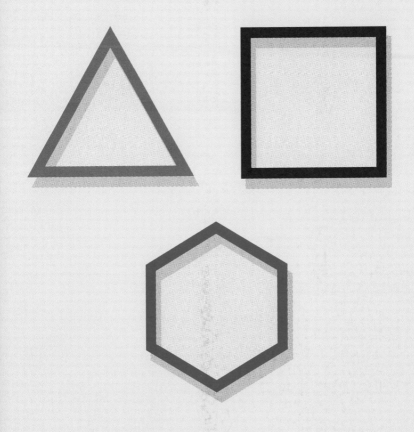

A quiver full of arrows. Which one is the odd one out?

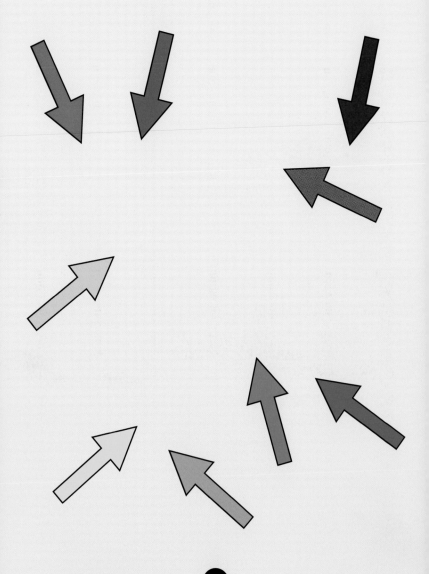

Each night, Arnold the Astronomer goes out to look at a particular constellation of stars.

Based on his observations for the first eight nights, can you guess what the next star group will look like?

The solid shape shown on this table will fall over once, but not a second time because it will then be stable.

Think about this: is it possible to design a multi-faceted solid shape that is unstable on every face?

As you while away the hours on a Sunday afternoon with the newspapers, you may have noticed that there are several ways of forming a crossword grid.

How many fundamentally different forms of symmetry are possible for a square crossword?

Baby Angus loves his new play mat but is annoyed that there appears to be a number missing from one of the shapes.

Can you identify the logic at work and recommend a number for Angus to try?

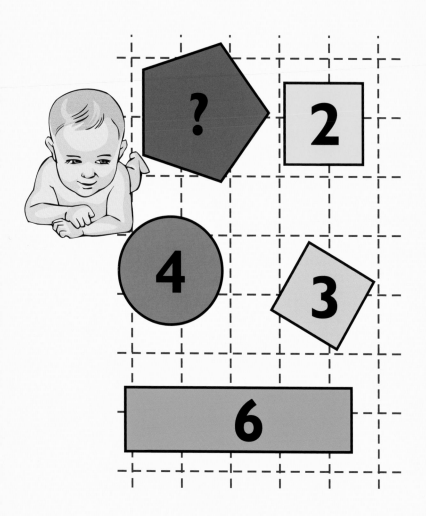

Here, the aim of the puzzle is getting from A to B, literally.

How many different routes are there for moving from A to B while following the arrows each time. Don't try to count them all – find a methodical system to give you the answer.

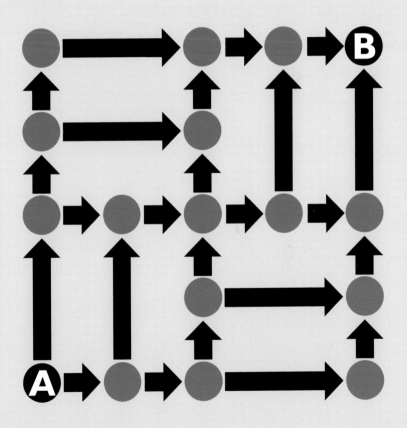

Jack was doodling in his geography class and was trying to find lots of silly shapes to draw.

As he had Mathematics last lesson, he knows that triangles usually contain a total internal angle of 180 degrees. Is it possible, he wondered, to draw a triangle on a piece of paper so that all three interior angles are right angles (90 degrees)?

What do you think?

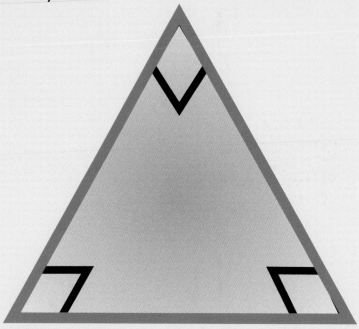

90 + 90 + 90 = 270?

Here are three half-dollars (worth 50 cents each) and three quarters (25 cents each). What is the least number of these coins that need to be moved so that both lines contain the same value?

Rearrange these letters so that a common eight-letter English word is formed.

Rearrange these letters to form the name of a well-known country.

Rearrange these diagrams into the correct well-known logical order. It doesn't matter where you start.

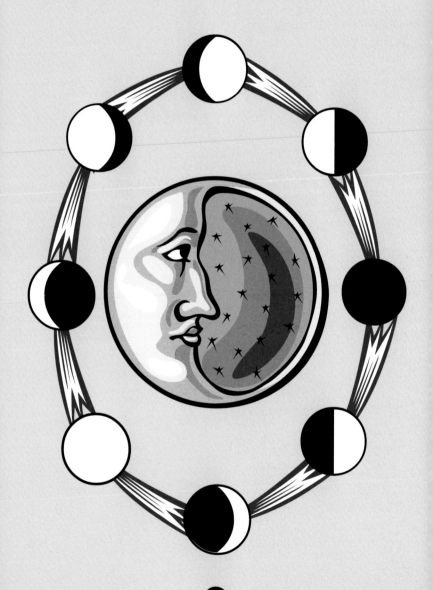

Make a third star, identical to the two that are already here, appear in front of your very eyes without altering the diagram in any way.

It is possible!

Sebiko, the chess Grand Master, was wondering about this little problem. Including the square you start on, what is the maximum number of squares that the knight can visit using his usual L-shaped move?

He may not visit any square more than once.

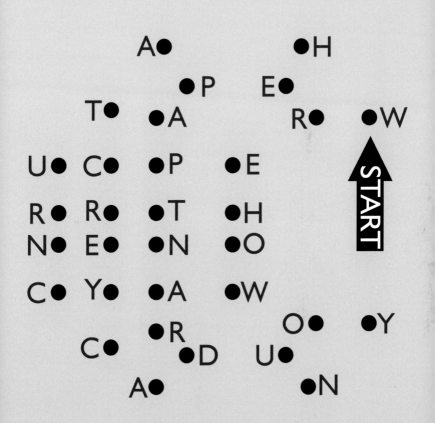

START

Here are two perfectly equilateral pyramids (tetrahedra).

(a) In volume terms, how many times bigger is the larger pyramid than the smaller pyramid?

(b) If you were to remove one small tetrahedron from each vertex (corner) of the larger tetrahedron, what shape remains?

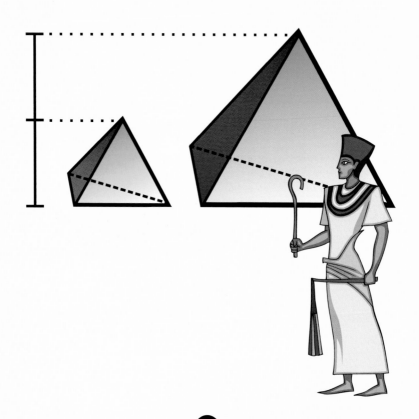

Rearrange these squares into their correct positions.

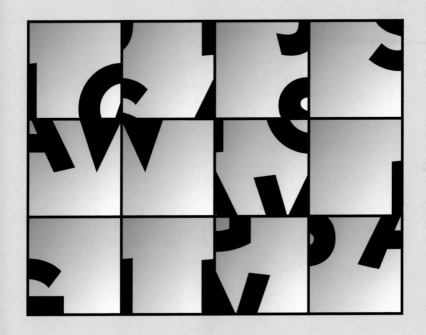

Why might cautious drivers in the US be insulted by this (real) car registration plate?

Curling is an increasingly popular sport thanks to its exciting finals at the Olympic Games. Kerry is trying to pack together her curling stones as tightly as possible.

(a) How many stones could she get in the white ring?

(b) How many could she fit into the red ring?

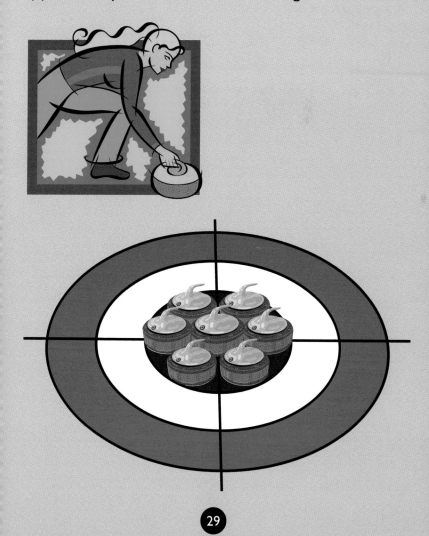

How large is the area of the red circle compared to the
yellow circle?

Yellow cab drivers cram the streets of New York which are laid out in grid fashion.

In this type of situation, known as 'taxicab geometry', you can only move along the grid lines (roads) shown. What would a **circle of radius two blocks** look like in taxicab geometry?

Starting hint: how is a circle defined in ordinary geometry?

= 1 block

Damien was putting up a special boutique wallpaper in his designer pad but it looks like he mixed up the rolls.

From left to right, in which order should the paper have been glued?

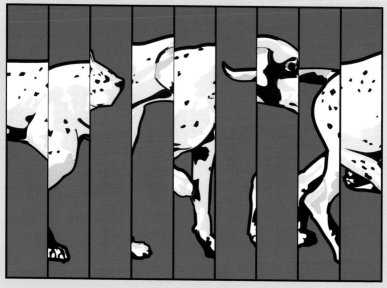

A B C D E F G H I

Which of these numbers is 'unreadable'?

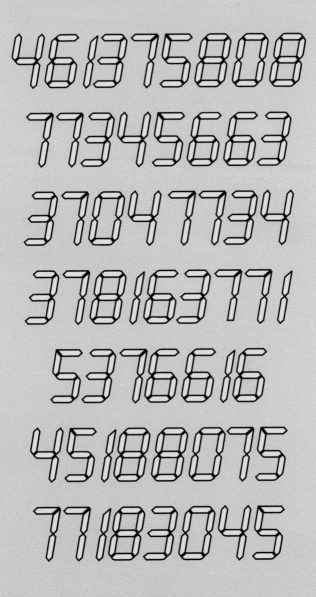

Carrie is a big fan of running theme nights. Tonight it's a medieval dinner party. She has a circular dining table, and requires that at least four people are sitting next to a knight and exactly three people are sitting next to a maiden.

What is the minimum number of people that Carrie will require at her dinner party?

(a) Draw four continuous (nose-to-tail) straight lines to connect all nine circles.

(b) Now do it again using a new line that only has three continuous straight lines.

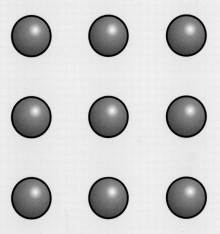

Which two adjacent lines on this page are the same size and perfectly parallel?

One part of each picture is similar. Place them in alphabetical order.

A gardener mows the grass on this lawn by visiting each square exactly once in a continuous loop so that he finishes where he started from.

As it happens, every other time that he turned 90 degrees along his route, that square contained a flower. Therefore, can you deduce which route he took through the lawn?

While taking one of many tea breaks, a bricklayer considers his bricks which are twice as long as they are wide.

When he completes a line of bricks, he has to do so at the correct height (shown by the dotted line). However, he notices that as he allows himself more bricks there are more possible ways of laying them out.

For example, with one brick there is just one way, but there are two possibilities for two bricks and three possibilities for three bricks.

(a) How many possibilities are there for four bricks?

(b) What about ten bricks? (Hint: try to work out the mathematical sequence)

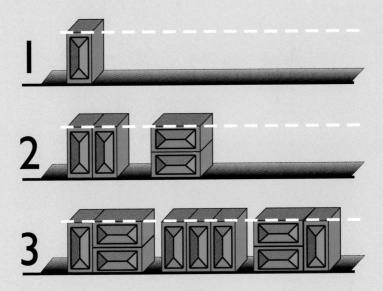

Here are eight different symbols commonly used in mathematics as a shorthand way of writing certain expressions.

How do these symbols make a fraction?

Q   *The set of rational numbers*

∪   *The union set*

O   *Zero*

⊥   *At right angles*

∥   *Parallel lines*

≡   *Identically equal to*

Z   *The set of integers*

⊥   *At right angles*

Keith was lost and, more infuriatingly, he couldn't fold his road map back up correctly.

How can he fold his map along lines A, B, C and D so that the pages run 1 to 8 from front to back? Assume that each page is printed on both sides and the orientation of the numbers doesn't matter.

What is the missing letter and where exactly should it be placed?

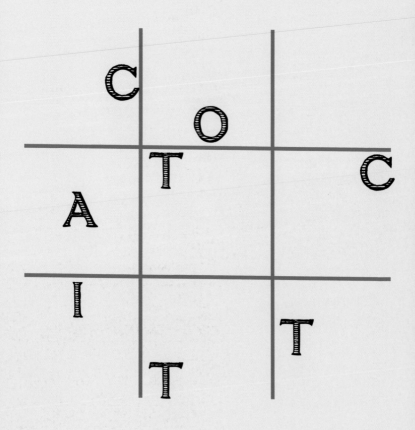

Gareth noticed that the logo on his beach towel seemed to have one letter stitched wrongly. 'No wonder it was so cheap,' he thought. In fact, there is a more rational explanation.

What is it?

Take a look at the situations in diagrams (a) and (b) then work out which way the scales will tilt in diagram (c).

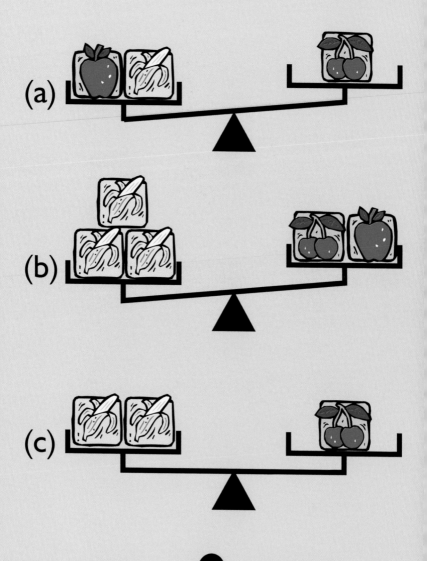

Which three **consecutive** letters of the standard English alphabet complete this word?

hazar___s

Harriet is making her own dress for a disco party tonight.

She has this triangular sheet of stickers which she has to cut along some of the lines shown to form smaller stickers of the same shape (i.e. an equilateral triangle).

How can Harriet cut up the sheet into the smallest number of equilateral triangles possible?

Oh dear, Biffo the clown has dropped all his juggling rings on the floor.

Can you tell which two are different from the rest?

Chi-Chi is the world's most intelligent panda. She can squirt water into the top of this bamboo pole and use it as a water clock. The water seeps out of the hole at the bottom. Each scratch up the pole denotes another 30 seconds of time.

What's wrong with Chi-Chi's water clock?

Wily William, a sign writer by trade, is offering a challenge to his current client who sells second-hand cars.

'Tell you what,' he says, 'I'll bet you can't add one more letter on this window to complete the word.'

How could you complete the challenge?

ITAMOTUA

What does this prove?

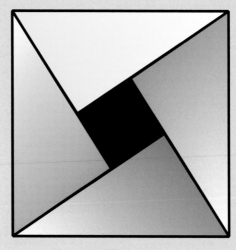

Fig. 1

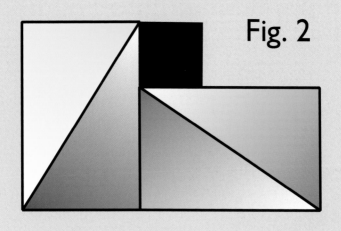

Fig. 2

Which number should replace X?

Think about this carefully: what is the smallest number of these coins that you need to move so that both squares contain the same number of heads and tails?

What should appear in the eighth box to complete the logic?

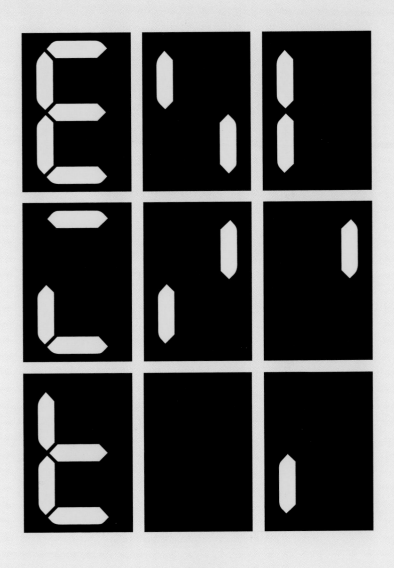

Which letter is missing from this special magic square?

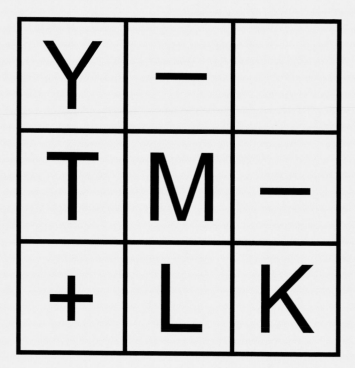

Y	–	
T	M	–
+	L	K

One 'circuit' consists of rolling the die forwards, right, backwards and left.

After how many circuits will the die be back to the same place and same orientation that it started from?

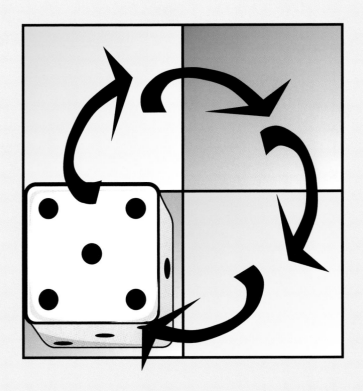

The Mad Scientist has two beakers full of a certain chemical with which he will rule the world. Assuming he has no other equipment available, what is the least number of beakers he needs to move so that only the second and fourth beakers in the row are full of the chemical?

This shape has six sides, all in the same plane.

Add three lines so that it now has six sides in different planes.

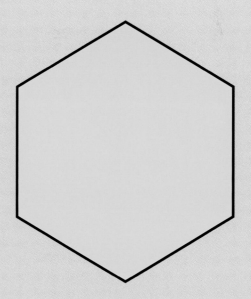

Which word can be read here?

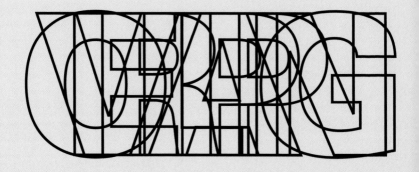

Two hummingbirds start side-by-side. They both fly for eight feet, turn 90 degrees to the right, then fly for another six feet.

What is the largest distance apart they could be now?

Class 4A2 were a little confused. Mr King had drawn this diagram on the blackboard and seemed satisfied with himself. 'Yes, I think that explains everything,' he claimed.

Can you tell the perplexed pupils what this diagram demonstrates?

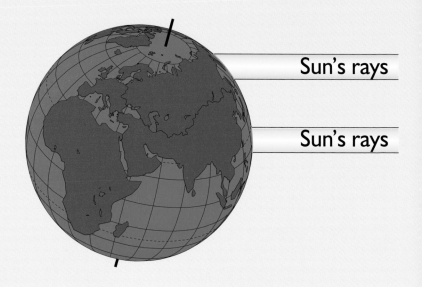

Sun's rays

Sun's rays

If these two planets complete their orbit every 6 and 8 years respectively, how long will it be before both planets and the sun are once again in a straight line?

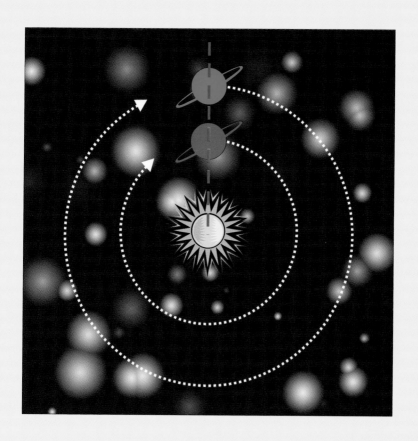

Clocks, like the one shown here, are seen at many railway stations. Each digit is made up of seven segments. Which individual segment is the most likely to wear out first?

Which piece of wire is in the middle of this stack?

This paper bag is sealed across the bottom edge, with corners at A and B.

If the top edge is sealed so that points C and D are its corners, what shape will the resulting bag take?

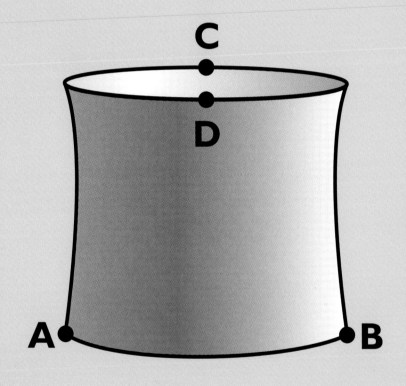

The Black Queens and White Queens have had an argument and don't want to appear on any square such that a Black Queen is attacking a White Queen or vice versa.

How could you fit three white queens and five black queens into a 5x5 board?

A solar-powered satellite is 50 million miles away from the Sun. What will have happened to the amount of light received by the satellite's solar panels when it is 100 million miles from the Sun?

You'll need to think about this puzzle in different ways.

How can you represent the number 10,000,000,000,000,000,000,000,000,000,000,000,000, 000,000,000,000,000,000,000,000,000,000,000,000,000, 000,000,000,000,000,000,000 on even the most basic type of (non-scientific) calculator?

'So you see, class, any section of a circle will look like any other similar-sized section of the circle. And more obviously, any part of a straight line looks like any other part of the line. Compare this with an ellipse, where some parts are flatter than others.'

After the teacher had finished, Patricia thought there might be a third shape that has this property although she wouldn't be able to draw it. Can you discover it too?

Billy Smart was feeling very smug as he had just received a brand new electric car racing set, where each of the two cars ride along metal runners. Their speed is controlled by handheld triggers.

Billy was enjoying planning a monster track that uses all the pieces in his set. Unfortunately for Billy, he's made a mistake in his design. What is it?

Use your head to discover what these objects have in common.

Which line is the odd one out? (Hint: pair them up)

Ariadne is surveying this giant sugar cube. To make sure she doesn't get stuck too easily, she is walking along the edges.

How many of the 12 edges could this spider crawl across before she is forced to retrace her steps?

Suppose you wanted to draw this grid but you only knew how to draw squares. What is the smallest number of squares you would need to draw? The answer is a lot less than 16.

What should be placed in the gap to complete something seen on roads?

ⅿOOH S

SI TNYMPHO

Zak Xylon, hero of the Universe, wishes to divide up this sector of space into eleven areas. How can he do it using four straight laser beams? The beams must start and end at one of the Suns (one will not be used).

Using a jigsaw power tool, how can a carpenter cut this piece of wood into two pieces of the same shape? He only needs to take his power tool through the wood once.

A scientist was looking at a DNA sample on a microscope slide. She found something very surprising – can you find it?

The extremely popular computer game Tetris uses five unique 'polyominoes' – multi-sided dominoes. In Tetris, polyominoes use four squares each. There are five unique designs, and seven if you count reflections as different.

How many different polyominoes can be formed from five identical squares if you (a) discount or (b) allow reflections?

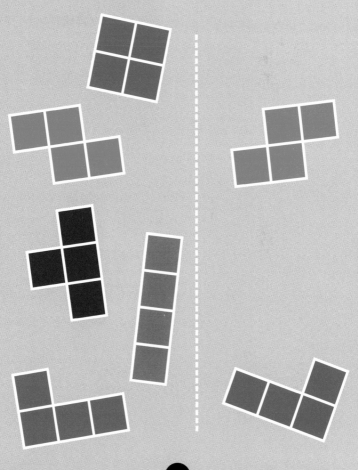

Slicing through a cone at different angles can produce a wide variety of curves (called conic sections) including a parabola, hyperbola, circle or ellipse.

How many shapes can you form by similarly slicing through a sphere at different places?

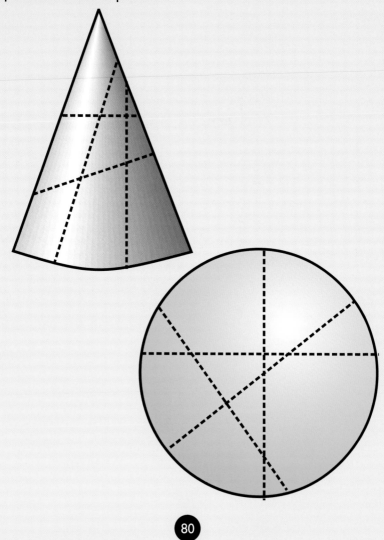

Which shapes should be shaded so that each row/column will contain the correct number of shaded squares?

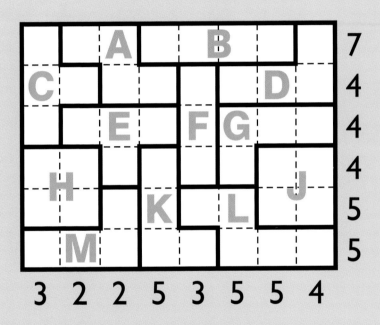

Remove six coins so that it becomes impossible to find a set of four coins that lie exactly on the corners of a square.

Two examples of what you have to **avoid** have been included in the illustration.

Find all the interior angles of the black triangle given that the other shapes are a regular hexagon, pentagon and equilateral triangle.

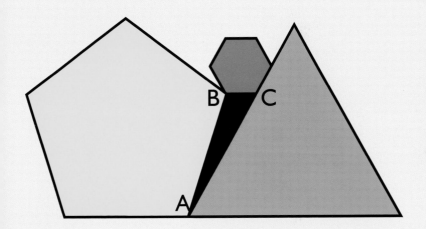

Each symbol represents a different number, and if two symbols are next to each other it is the same as adding the numbers together.

What is the value of the final line, expressed using the fewest symbols possible?

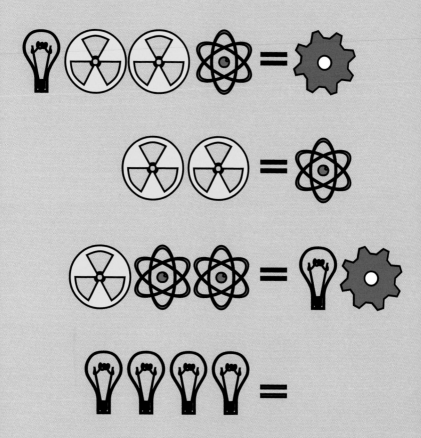

This blue cheese has a rectangle cut out of it. You need to use one cut to slice the cheese into two pieces of equal volume.

Can you find **two** solutions?

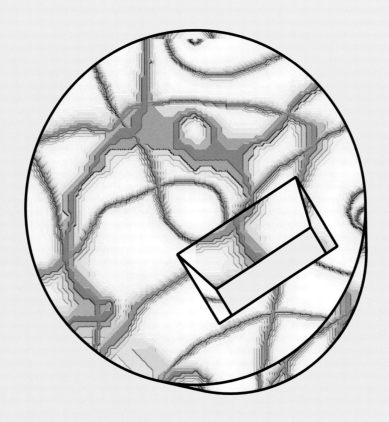

This printer only has one letterhead and one blank continuation page in its paper tray (in some order).

If I print a two-page letter, what is the probability that it will be printed correctly?

How can the bookworm crawl over every white line exactly once without crossing over the blue area?

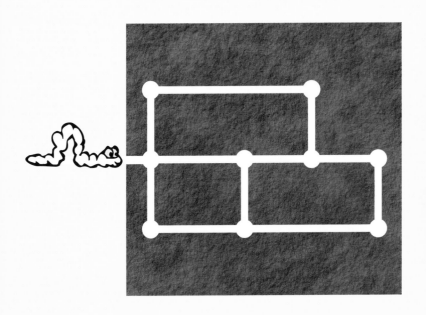

How many 3 x 1 planks (like the example shown) can you cut from the larger sheet?

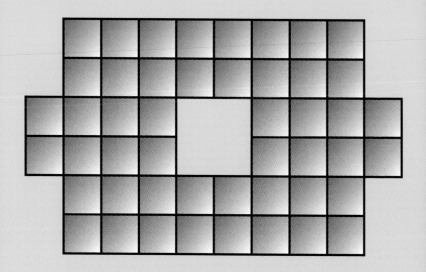

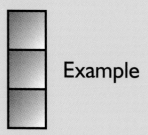
Example

The EconoCorp company is an innovative institution committed to designing efficient products. Their latest target is the ruler business, because of the number of marks on them that are not needed. For example, the distance between 1 and 2 inches is the same as 3 and 4 inches.

Where would the EconoCorp company draw three more vertical lines on this ruler so that each pair of marks measures a unique linear distance in whole units?

For example, drawing the lines at 4, 5 and 7 wouldn't work because 0–4 is the same distance as 7–11.

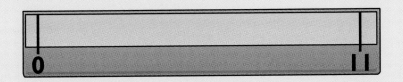

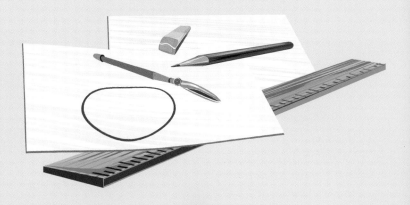

A town planner notices that there are only two **fundamentally different** ways of connecting four cities together with three city-to-city roads. These are shown below.

(a) How many fundamentally different ways are there of connecting five cities using four roads?

(b) What about six cities with five roads?

Timmy wasn't very good at doing up the laces on his training shoes.

When the string is pulled taut, will a knot be formed?

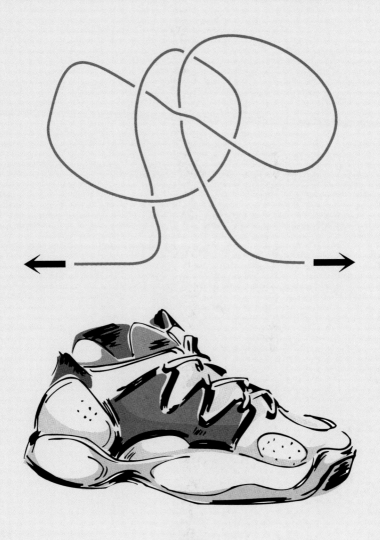

The worker bee is feeling a bit dizzy (he had a bit too much nectar last night). Logically, which honeycomb segment should he go to next?

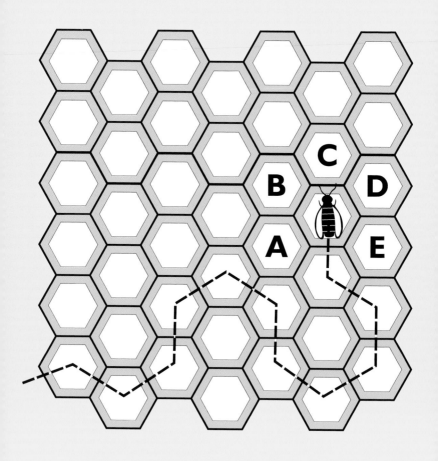

Determine which of these shapes represents the first letter of the English alphabet:

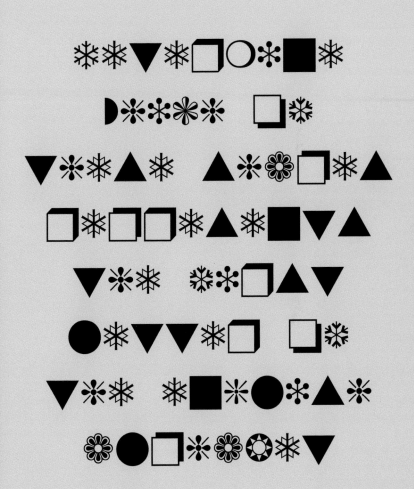

How can you cut this square piece of wood into three squares using two straight cuts and sticking two edges together with glue?

Which of these objects would be the best logical fit with the items illustrated below: a potato, a bookmark, a clock or a knife?

(a) Shade in five circles on this diagram so that there is one shaded circle in every line (in all three directions):

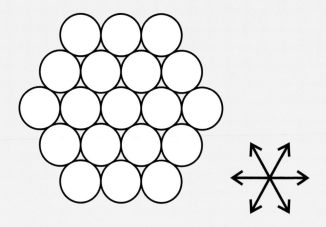

(b) Shade in 14 circles on this diagram so that there are two shaded circles in every line (in all three directions):

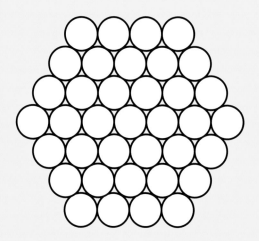

The circumference (edge) of this square has been divided into five equal lengths. From those points, a line has been drawn to the middle of the square.

Prove that each section of the square has the same area.

1. Start at 12 o'clock.

2. Think of one of the numbers on the clock.

3. Move one hour clockwise for every letter in your number.

4. You will land on a new number. Repeat step 3 for that number.

5. You will land on a third number. Repeat step 3 for this number.

Which hour have you finished up on?

If this silhouette is enlarged by 200%, as shown, what happens to the area and perimeter respectively?

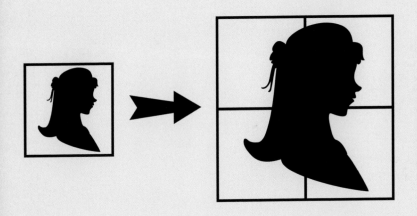

Whimper, the useless ghost, cannot travel through walls. The floor plan of the mansion which Whimper haunts is given below.

Which doorway needs to be bricked up so that Whimper could haunt the entire mansion by floating through every doorway exactly once from any starting point?

ANSWERS

ANSWERS TO PUZZLES ENDING IN –1

1 Because of the curvature of the Earth, the shortest distance will actually appear curved on most projection maps. Hence, pilots fly along a path similar to that shown by route B because it is the shortest.

11 They tesselate – in other words, you could completely fill a flat plane with tiles of one of these shapes, without leaving any gaps.

21 As well as turning some letters upside-down, the ambiguity of the typeface (between a capital 'i' and a small 'L') is exploited. The answer is:

Ireland

31 Imagine the grid is a city map and a taxi begins at the middle point. The circle of radius two blocks is the collection of eight points that are any combination of two blocks away. All eight points lie on a square tilted at 45 degrees, as shown:

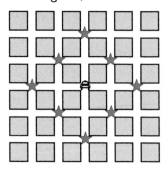

Note that in taxicab geometry, the circle is in fact a set of discrete points rather than a continuous line.

41 Here's the diagram again for reference:

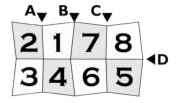

Fold 2 and 3 forward (along fold A), fold 8 and 5 back (fold C), fold bottom half up (fold D) then close both halves like a book (fold B).

51 54 is missing. They are the numbers of a typical Snakes and Ladders board.

100	99	98	97	96	95	94	93	92	91
81	82	83	84	85	86	87	**88**	89	90
80	**79**	78	77	76	75	74	73	72	71
61	62	**63**	64	65	66	67	68	69	70
60	59	58	57	56	55	**54**	53	52	51
41	42	43	44	45	46	47	48	49	50
40	39	38	37	36	35	34	33	32	31
21	22	23	24	25	26	27	28	29	30
20	19	18	17	16	15	14	**13**	12	11
1	2	3	4	5	6	7	8	9	10

61 The answer is 12 years. Each year the angular difference between the planets rises by 15 degrees. This is because in one year, one planet has moved by 360/6 = 60 degrees but the other has only moved by 360/8 = 45 degrees.

After 12 years this difference is 180 degrees, so they are in a straight line again but the planets are on different sides of the sun.

71 The blue line shown is the odd one out. It is not perpendicular to any other line. The rest of the lines cross at right angles with one other line.

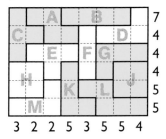

81 Shade in shapes A, B, C, G, J, K and L:

	3	2	2	5	3	5	5	4	
	A		B						7
C							D		4
		E		F	G				4
									4
	H			K	L		J		5
	M								5

91 Yes, a simple 'overhand knot' will be formed.

ANSWERS TO PUZZLES ENDING IN –2

2 They all use or contain bulbs.

12 The red arrow does not point to the tail of another arrow.

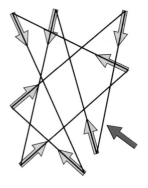

22 They are the phases of the Moon. If we choose to start at Full Moon, the sequence goes:

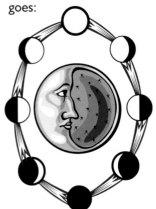

32 The correct order is shown below:

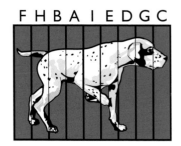

F H B A I E D G C

42 A letter E should be placed in the bottom-right corner of the empty square. If you overlap all nine squares (as if they were printed on clear plastic) it spells out TIC TAC TOE.

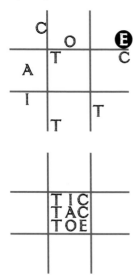

52 Only one coin needs to be moved. Take a tail from the blue square and balance it on edge on the adjoining line with the tails side facing towards the red square. Both squares now have two tails and two heads.

62 If you examine how many times the segments change as they count through the digits, you will find that the lower-left segment changes state far more times than any other. Therefore, the lower-left segment of the final digit will probably wear out first because it flips over a staggering 69,120 times every day!

72 The best she can do is nine edges before she revisits an edge that she's already been to.

82 Here is one possible solution:

92 Hexagon D should be next. The pattern goes: turn right x 1, left x 2, right x 3, left x 4, right x 5.

3   Ten in total – nine obvious
    arrows plus another one
    pointing in the opposite
    direction:

13 They are the letters A to I,
    with a star marking every
    endpoint or line junction:

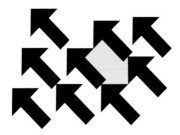

23 Cross your eyes until the
    stars overlap! You can now
    see three stars even though
    you know there are really
    only two.

33 The fourth one reads
    ILLEGIBLE when upside-
    down. Note that the other
    numbers also form words.

SHOEBILL
SLOBBISH
GIGGLES
ILLEGIBLE
HELLHOLE
EGGSHELL
BOBSLEIGH

43 In fact, it was stitched
    correctly. He was just
    looking at it from the wrong
    side. If he flipped the towel
    over about a horizontal
    axis, both words would
    look correct:

53 The calculator segments shown are those that are not lit when displaying the digits from 1 to 9.

Since 8 uses all the segments, there are none left unused so the empty box should be left blank.

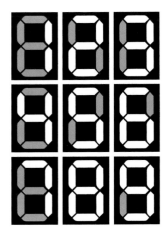

63 The order of the overlapping wires from the top of the pile down is C, B, A, G, D, E, F, so G is in the middle.

73 Six squares are needed. One way is: a 3 x 3 square in the four corners, then a 2 x 2 square in two opposite corners. The squares have been offset slightly for clarity.

83 Internal angle of regular pentagon = 108 degrees. (You can work this out by dividing the shape into five triangles).

Hence, angle of black triangle at corner A = 180 − 108 − 60 = 12. Angle at corner C = 60. So, angle at corner B must be 180 − 12 − 60 = 108.

93 This is simply a cryptogram of the question ('Determine which of these...') where each letter has been replaced by a different symbol. Hence, A is the first symbol of the last word (❀).

ANSWERS TO PUZZLES ENDING IN –4

4 Silhouette:

14 No, otherwise you would have invented perpetual motion.

24 A maximum of 15 squares, including the one you start on. There's no way of visiting the whole board, regardless of which route you take.

34 Five – arrange them as shown (K=knight, M=maiden).

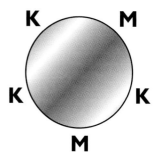

Note that if the word 'exactly' wasn't in the question, knight-knight-maiden-maiden would have been an acceptable arrangement.

44 Consider diagram (a). If A + B > C, then it follows that B > C – A. Adding this to diagram (b) 3B > A + C gives 4B > 2C.

Dividing by two on either side, 2B > C which is the same as diagram (c). Therefore, the left pan is heavier.

54 This a magic square in that every row and column contains two diagonal lines, three vertical lines and two horizontal lines.

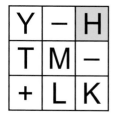

Therefore, H must be missing as it is the only

letter you can make using the two vertical and one horizontal lines missing from the relevant rows and columns.

64 A tetrahedron (triangle-based pyramid). This is how the new-style 'pyramid' tea bags are made.

74 An upside-down C, to complete the word SCHOOL which is sometimes painted on the road.

84 Substitute equations 1 and 2 into equation 3 to give 5 Radiations = 2 Bulbs + 4 Radiations, or 2 Bulbs = 1 Radiation. Now consider equation 4:

4 Bulbs = 2 Radiations but, by equation 2, this equals 1 Atom so that's the answer.

94 Cut one-third of the way along its length then one-third of the way along its breadth. This gives two squares and two rectangles. Glue the two rectangles together to give the third square.

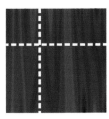

ANSWERS TO PUZZLES ENDING IN –5

5 Eight in total. There's no match between the 1 and 6 faces. Two spots on the 2 match two on the 5 and similarly two spots on the 3 match two on the 4.

15 Four (five if you include 'no symmetry'): quarter-turn, half-turn, left/right reflected, top/bottom reflected.

25 The fact that there was no question is deliberate. Starting where indicated, you can spell out the question 'What currency can you draw on the paper'. If you follow this sequence like a dot-to-dot, you will have drawn the Euro sign:

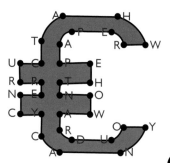

35 (a) This is a very traditional puzzle:

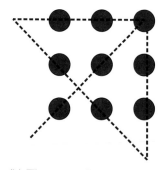

(b) This one takes more lateral thought:

45 Turn 'nop' upside-down to complete 'hazardous'.

hazardous

55 Three – each circuit has the effect of a 120 degree turn about one diagonal.

65 Here is one possible solution, although others exist:

A B C D E

	A	B	C	D	E	
1		♛			♛	**1**
2					♛	**2**
3	♛					**3**
4	♛			♛		**4**
5			♛	♛		**5**

75 The question reads:

If you take these strips and rearrange them to form a basic question, which common English word is spelled out?

H Y P N O T I S M

As you can see from the letters at the bottom, the word HYPNOTISM has been formed.

85 (a) Cut horizontally, parallel with the table.

(b) Cut along the whole cake, through the line that joins the middle of the circle with the rectangle's middle.

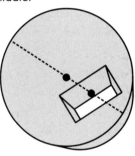

95 A bookmark would fit best – they are all objects specifically designed to be used with one other object (lock, lips, teeth, cork, arrow).

ANSWERS TO PUZZLES ENDING IN –6

6   If you place the 'mask' over the letters in three different orientations, you get a THREE PIECE SUITE.

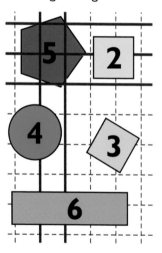

16 Five, because it cuts through five of the lines in the background grid:

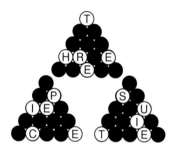

26 (a) If you double the height, width and breadth of any 3D object, you will increase the volume by eight times.

(b) You will be left with an octahedron, which looks like two square-based pyramids stuck together:

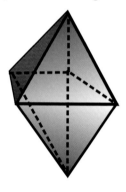

36 The two letter 'L's in the word 'parallel'.

46 The best Harriet can do is to split it up into eight triangles as shown below:

56 One – pour the contents of the 5th glass into the 3rd glass then place this glass (now empty) on the left of the 1st glass.

66 It will fall to a quarter of its initial value. This is a consequence of a sphere's surface area being proportional to the radius squared.

Here is a demonstration of the reason in picture form. Each set of squares is an equal distance apart but the area increases by a square amount (1, 4, 9, 16...)

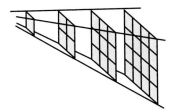

76 Here is one possibility:

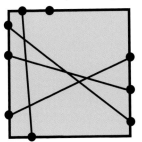

86 Chance that text appears on correct side of letterhead = $\frac{1}{2}$.

Chance that text is right way up = $\frac{1}{2}$.

Chance that pages are printed in correct order = $\frac{1}{2}$.

Hence, overall chance = $\frac{1}{2} \times \frac{1}{2} \times \frac{1}{2} = 1/8$.

96 (a)

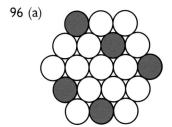

(b)

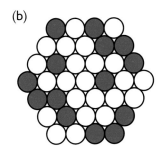

ANSWERS TO PUZZLES ENDING IN –7

7 Cut into quarters then do a circular cut. (This final cut would have a diameter of 8.485 inches for a 12 inch pizza.)

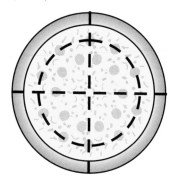

17 There is only one way of reaching the left or bottom edge. At every other junction, add together the numbers leading into it. The answer is 13.

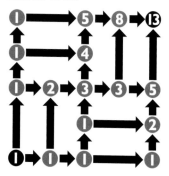

27 Appropriately enough, the word JIGSAW is written on the intersections of the squares.

37 HEEL (from the shoe), KEEL (from the ship), PEEL (from the banana), REEL (from the film).

47 The red and blue rings on the right-hand side are linked.

The rest of the circles are merely laid one on top of each other.

57 Draw three straight lines as shown. You now have a cube.

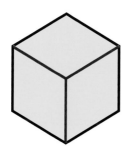

67 Enter 706006 (or 709009) and turn it upside-down to give 'GOOGOL' – which is the word that describes 1 followed by 100 zeroes.

77 One piece is a mirror image of the other:

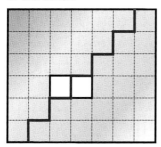

87 At some point the worm must eat through the paper, crawl along the back, then reappear elsewhere in the diagram.

97 Each section has the same base (as given in the question) and the same perpendicular height (distance from the middle to the edge measured perpendicularly, as shown). Therefore, each section must have the same area.

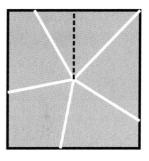

If you don't agree, divide each section into four smaller triangles – these definitely have the same base and height so the areas of any set of four triangles is the same.

ANSWERS TO PUZZLES ENDING IN –8

8   When she stamps it on to a piece of paper, the imprint will look like:

HAИИAH

18 Yes, if the piece of paper is spherical such as a globe. Draw from its 'North Pole' down to the equator, along a quarter of the equator, then back up to the North.

Since the angle at which the lines join at each vertex is 90 degrees, the whole triangle contains 270 degrees.

A triangle of this nature is described as being 'trirectangular'.

28 Because they would see MOVE IT in their rear-view mirror:

38 A fat H-shape is formed, as shown:

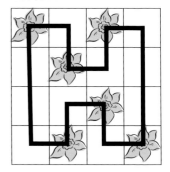

48 Water pressure decreases as the height of the water falls.

Therefore, the scratches on the pole should get closer together towards the end, as shown on the right:

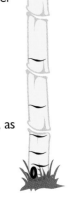

58 The word that can be read is OVERLAPPING. We'll prove this by separating the letters a little:

68 Patricia couldn't strictly draw it on the blackboard because it is a 3D shape.

Any section of this spiral will look like any other section of the same size:

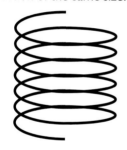

78 The DNA sample actually spells out the words that make up the abbreviation DNA, namely DEOXY-RIBONUCLEIC ACID

DEOXYRIBONUCLEIC ACID

This is easier to spot if you hold the book flat and level with your eyes then look down the page.

88 The trick is to shade in the squares as shown. No matter where you place the 3x1 plank, it will always cover a yellow, blue and red square.

Since there are only 14 red squares, then 14 planks is the maximum possible.

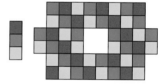

98 Strangely, no matter which number you choose at step 2, you will always end up at 1 o'clock.

For example, suppose the number you choose is 7 (SEVEN). You'd spell out S-E-V-E-N to end up at 5 o'clock. Spelling out F-I-V-E takes you to 9 o'clock. Finally, spelling out N-I-N-E lands you at 1 o'clock.

ANSWERS TO PUZZLES ENDING IN –9

9 Two-thirds. The outer square is blue (so add 1) but the yellow square inside that is yellow (subtract ½) but half of that yellow square is blue (add ¼) and so on. The pattern goes:

$1 - ½ + ¼ - 1/8 + 1/16... = 2/3$ (after infinitely many squares).

19 Move any of the half-dollars and place it over the top of the quarter on the left or right. Each line now contains $1.25.

29 (a) 12, and (b) 18. Each time the radius increases by one stone, the number of stones you can fit increases by six.

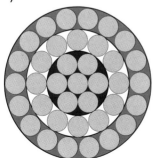

39 (a) Five solutions when there are four bricks.

(b) Extending the series further, you will find that the results are the Fibonacci series where each number equals the sum of the previous two:

$1 + 2 = 3$
$2 + 3 = 5$
$3 + 5 = 8$
$5 + 8 = 13$ etc.

This gives the series 1, 2, 3, 5, 8, 13, 21, 34, 55, 89, 144 and so on.

89 is the tenth term in this list, hence 89 solutions exist for ten bricks.

49 Add a backward 'C' on the left-hand side. The word AUTOMATIC can be read on the other side of the window.

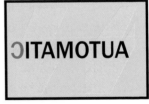

59 The animal featured in this puzzle was a clue – hummingbirds are famous for their ability to fly backwards.

Therefore, even if they begin by facing the same way, they could be far apart after flying 6+8=14 feet.

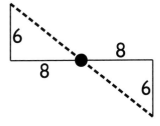

This gives us two right angles. By Pythagoras, we can calculate that they are 10 feet away from their start point, or 20 feet apart from each other.

69 The odd number of cross-over pieces has created, in effect, a short circuit. In other words, there is only one track, not two. Either controller would move both cars. This arrangement is called a Möbius loop.

79 There are 12 unique designs (illustrated), which rises to 18 if you include reflections.

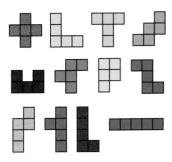

89 One solution is at 1, 4 and 9 units. Using this ruler, you can measure every unit length from 1 to 11 except 6.

99 The area quadruples and the perimeter doubles. You can see this demonstrated by the squares that were used in the illustration – there are now 4 squares (was 1) with perimeter 8 (was 4).

ANSWERS TO PUZZLES ENDING IN –0

10 E and F, as shown below:

20 Some letters need to be turned upside-down:

elephant

30 Note that the green triangle is one quarter the size of the blue triangle, hence the yellow circle is one quarter the size of red circle too.

40 If you rotate some symbols and push them together as shown, you will find that they form a QUOTIENT (meaning 'fraction'):

QUOTIENT

50 The area of Figure I is the square of the hypotenuse of any of the triangles.

In Figure 2, we see that this same area can be re-arranged into two squares that we can separate by a dotted line:

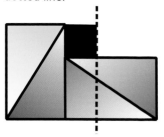

We now see that this is in fact two squares. The one on the left has a side equal to the middle length of the triangle, and the one on the right has a side equal to the shortest length. Thus, the square of the hypotenuse equals the sum of the squares of the other two sides.

This completes one of many proofs of Pythagoras's Theorem.

60 Near the Equator, the Sun's rays are relatively concentrated (red line). Away from the Equator, the rays of the same width cover less area (orange line).

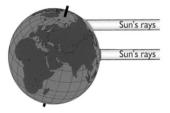

Hence, it explains why the Earth is hotter nearer the Equator. (Since the Earth 'wobbles' on its axis, this also explains why seasons occur.)

70 They all contain parts of the head: a bottle has a neck, a needle has an eye, a clock has a face, a plane has a nose, a comb has teeth and a river has a head and a mouth.

80 No matter what angle you slice at, it will always form a circular cross-section. Buy an Edam cheese and try it for yourself.

90 (a) Three ways:

(b) Six.

100 The right-hand door in the bottom-right room. It is the only adjoining door between two rooms containing an odd number of doors.

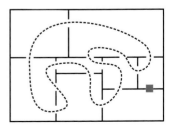

ABOUT THE AUTHOR

David J. Bodycombe was born in Darlington, England, in 1973. Over many years his creations have appeared in various TV and radio programmes, print media, board games, web sites, advertising campaigns and more.

He has contributed to numerous UK television shows including *Treasure Hunt* (BBC 2), *The Mole* (Channel 5), *Starfinder* (ITV), *Inside Clyde* (Disney) and five series of *The Crystal Maze* (Channel 4).

On BBC Radio 4 he appears on the problem solving show *Puzzle Panel*, and is also the researcher and question setter for the treasure hunt game *X Marks the Spot*.

David has authored many highly acclaimed puzzle books, and writes over 1000 puzzles a year for columns in periodicals such as the *Big Issue*, *Metro* and *Ireland on Sunday*.

After graduating in Mathematics from the University of Durham, David now runs Labyrinth Games, a games design consultancy, from his base in London.

Web site: www.labyrinthgames.com